A NOTE TO PARENTS

Early Step into Reading Books are designed for preschoolers and kindergartners who are just getting ready to read. The words are easy, the type is big, and the stories are packed with rhyme, rhythm, and repetition.

We suggest that you read this book to your child the first few times, pointing to each word as you go. Soon your child will start saying the words with you. And before long, he or she will try to read the story alone. Don't be surprised if your child uses the pictures to figure out the text—that's what they're there for! The important thing is to develop your child's confidence—and to show your child that reading is fun.

When your child is ready to move on, try the rest of the steps in our Step into Reading series. **Step 1 Books** (preschool–grade 1) feature the same easy-to-read type as the Early Step into Reading Books, but with more words per page. **Step 2 Books** (grades 1–3) are both longer and slightly more difficult, while **Step 3 Books** (grades 2–3) introduce readers to paragraphs and fully developed plot lines. **Step 4 Books** (grades 2–4) offer exciting nonfiction for the increasingly independent reader.

For Chip, who likes to yak.
—C. G.

For Steven Kamenir
—B. L.

Text copyright © 1999 by Charles Ghigna. Illustrations copyright © 1999 by Brian Lies.
All rights reserved under International and Pan-American Copyright Conventions. Published in the United States by Random House, Inc., New York, and simultaneously in Canada by Random House of Canada Limited, Toronto.

Library of Congress Cataloging-in-Publication Data
Ghigna, Charles. See the yak yak / by Charles Ghigna ; illustrated by Brian Lies.
    p. cm. — (Early step into reading) SUMMARY: Illustrations and brief text present pairs of words that are spelled the same but have different meanings.
ISBN 0-679-89135-8 (pbk.) — ISBN 0-679-99135-2 (lib. bdg.)
1. English language—Homonyms—Juvenile literature. [1. English language—Homonyms.]
I. Lies, Brian, ill. II. Title. III. Series. PE1595.G45 1999 428.1—dc21 98-41044

www.randomhouse.com/kids

Printed in the United States of America 10 9 8 7 6 5 4 3 2 1

STEP INTO READING is a registered trademark and EARLY STEP INTO READING and colophon are trademarks of Random House, Inc.

Early Step into Reading™

See the Yak Yak

by Charles Ghigna
illustrated by Brian Lies

Random House 🏠 New York

See the yak yak.

See the steer steer.

See the skate skate.

See the badger badger.

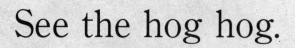

See the hog hog.

See the chicken chicken.

See the ram ram.

See the buck buck.

See the bare bear.

See the bat bat.

See the swallow swallow.

See the seal seal.

See the bug bug.

See the slug slug.

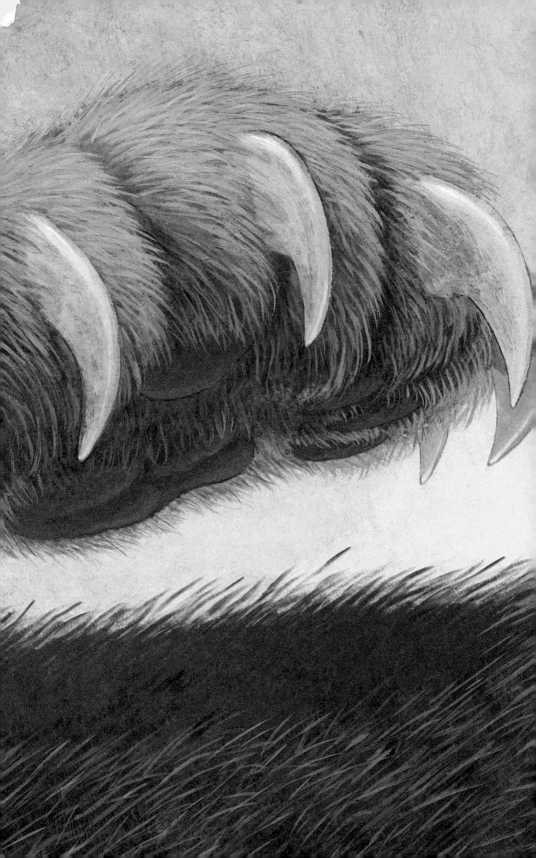

See the flea flee.

See the fly fly.

See the duck duck.

See the kid kid.

See the rain rain.

See the flower flower.

See the fish fish.

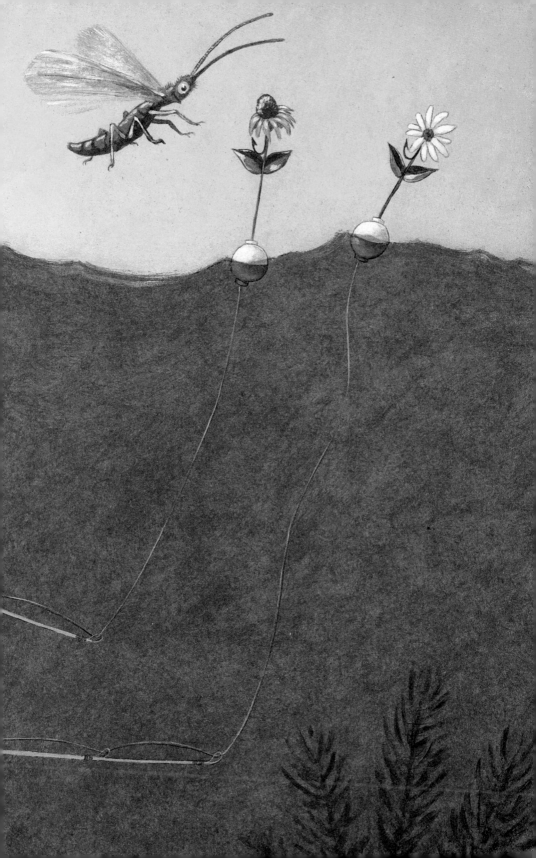

See the end end.